W9-AJT-143

J
P

11,852

Preston, Edna Mitchell
    The sad story of the little bluebird and the
hungry cat. Illustrated by Barbara Cooney.
N.Y., Four Winds press, [1975]
    unp.   col.illus.

    I.Cooney, Barbara, illus.   II.Title.

The Sad Story of the Little Bluebird and the Hungry Cat

by Edna Mitchell Preston • illustrated by Barbara Cooney

Four Winds Press   New York

LIBRARY OF CONGRESS CATALOGING IN PUBLICATION DATA

Preston, Edna Mitchell.
    The sad story of the little bluebird and the hungry cat.

    SUMMARY: A hungry cat hops, skips, and jumps after a bluebird.
Then the bluebird begins to fly.
    I. Cooney, Barbara.   II. Title.
PZ8.3.P913Sad [E] 75-12570
ISBN 0-590-07370-2

PUBLISHED BY FOUR WINDS PRESS

A DIVISION OF SCHOLASTIC MAGAZINES, INC., NEW YORK, N.Y.

TEXT COPYRIGHT © 1975 BY EDNA MITCHELL PRESTON

ILLUSTRATIONS COPYRIGHT © 1975 BY BARBARA COONEY PORTER

ALL RIGHTS RESERVED

PRINTED IN THE UNITED STATES OF AMERICA

LIBRARY OF CONGRESS CATALOG NUMBER: 75-12570

1 2 3 4 5   79 78 77 76 75

A little bluebird was hopping along
hopping along
hopping along
A little bluebird was hopping along
singing a happy hopping song,
"I can hop. Can you?"

A hungry cat came hopping behind
                    hopping behind
                    hopping behind
A hungry cat came hopping behind
                    singing a hungry song,
                    "You can hop. I can, too."

The hungry cat came hopping behind
And he had breakfast on his mind
Hopping along
Singing a hungry song,
"I think my breakfast is going to be YOU."

Hop   hop   hop   went the little bluebird.
HOP   HOP   HOP   went the hungry cat.

HOP!

BUT –

The little bluebird was skipping along
skipping along
skipping along
The little bluebird was skipping along
singing a happy skipping song,
"I can skip. Can you?"

The hungry cat came skipping behind
skipping behind
skipping behind
The hungry cat came skipping behind
singing a hungry song,
"You can skip. I can, too."

The hungry cat came skipping behind
And he had lunch on his mind
Skipping along
Singing a hungry song,
"I think my lunch is going to be YOU."

Skip   skip   skip   went the little bluebird.
SKIP   SKIP   SKIP   went the hungry cat.

SKIP   **SKOP!**

BUT –

The little bluebird was jumping along
jumping along
jumping along
The little bluebird was jumping along
singing a happy jumping song,
"I can jump. Can you?"

The hungry cat came jumping behind
　　　　jumping behind
　　　　jumping behind
The hungry cat came jumping behind
　　　　singing a hungry song,
　　　　"You can jump. I can, too."

The hungry cat came jumping behind
And he had supper on his mind
Jumping along
Singing a hungry song,
"I think my supper is going to be YOU."

Jump   jump   jump   went the little bluebird.
JUMP   JUMP   JUMP   went the hungry cat.

JUMP!

BUT –

   The little bluebird was flying along
                              flying along
                              flying along
   The little bluebird was flying along
                              singing a happy flying song,
                              "I can fly. Can you?"

The hungry cat was left behind
                    left behind
                    left behind
The hungry cat was left behind
                    singing a hungry song.

"Oh, I am a hungry cat I am.
 Oh, a hungry cat am I.

I can hop.
I can skip.
I can jump.
I can run.
But –
I can not
I can not
I can not fly."

So –

The hungry cat went running home
running home
running home
The hungry cat went running home
singing a hungry HUNGRY song,

"Meow...meow...meow..."